FAITH AND FREED(

These Are Our Neighbors
REVISED EDITION

Sister M. Marguerite, S.N.D., M.A.

Sister M. Bernarda, C.PP.S., PH.D.

GINN AND COMPANY
Boston • New York • Chicago • Atlanta
Dallas • Palo Alto • Toronto

ACKNOWLEDGMENTS

Grateful acknowledgment is made to the following authors and pub-lishers for permission to use copyrighted materials: Abelard-Schuman, Ltd., for "New House," reprinted by permission of the publisher, Abelard-Schuman, Ltd., from *Up the Windy Hill,* by Aileen Fisher, copyright 1953, by Aileen Fisher; E. P. Dutton & Co., Inc., and J. M. Dent & Sons, Ltd., for "Christ Our King," from the book *The Wild Knight and Other Poems,* by G. K. Chesterton, published by E. P. Dutton & Co., Inc., and reprinted with their permission; Ginn and Company for "The Little Soldier," by Carolyn S. Bailey, from *The Children's Book-shelf; J. B.* Lippincott Company for "Mrs. Goose and the Rain," adapted from "Showers and Sunshine," in *Hello, Mrs. Goose,* by Miriam Clark Potter, copyright 1947 by Miriam Clark Potter, and published by J. B. Lippincott Company; The <u>Macmillan</u> Company for "Angels," from *The Child On His Knees,* by Mary Dixon Thayer, copyright and used with the permission of The Macmillan Company; The McBride Company, Inc., New York, and Gerald Duckworth & Co., Ltd., London, for "The Birds," from *Sonnets and Verse,* by Hilaire Belloc, reprinted by permis-sion; Frederick Pustet Company, Inc., for "Saint Francis and the Birds," adapted from A *Garland of Saints for Children,* by Rev. M. A. Chapman.

Acknowledgment is made to the following authors and to *Jack and* Jill for selections adapted and reprinted by special permission of and copyright by The Curtis Publishing Company: The Estate of Steve Benedict for "The Cows' Shawl," from "Bossy's Shawl," © 1952; Helen Boyd Dyer for "The Hacker-Crackers' Busy Day," from "The Rum-mely-Pummely's Busy Day," © 1947; John E. Elwood for "The Wise Little Owl," from "Little Gray Owl," ©) 1950; Victoria Gunsolus for "The Twins' Birthday Surprise," from "Weezie's Birthday," © 1953; Franklin P. Harry for "Bobby Squirrel's Funny Tail," from "Archie's Tail Is Turning Green," © 1951; Mary L. Hintz for "Hefty's Singing," © 1950; Flora Gregg Iliff for "Uncle Tom's Surprise," from "Uncle John's Talking Well," © 1953; Rose Leion for "Jean and the Book-mobile," from "Ellie Lou and the Bookmobile," © 1953; Claire Trask for "The Robber Family," © 1954.

[Continued on page 256)

FAITH AND FREEDOM

NIHIL OBSTAT:

Rev. Gerard Sloyan, s.t.l., ph.d., CENSOR DEPUTATUS

IMPRIMATUR:

† Patrick A. O'Boyle, d.d., ARCHBISHOP OF WASHINGTON

Washington, December 15, 1961

COMMISSION ON AMERICAN CITIZENSHIP
THE CATHOLIC UNIVERSITY OF AMERICA

Rt. Rev. Msgr. William J. McDonald, *President of the Commission*

Rt. Rev. Msgr. Joseph A. Gorham, *Director*

Katherine Rankin, *Editorial Consultant*

Sister Mary Lenore, o.p., *Curriculum Consultant*

PUBLISHED FOR THE CATHOLIC UNIVERSITY OF AMERICA PRESS
WASHINGTON, D.C.

Contents

■ We Live Together

■ New Neighbors

◼ School Neighbors

◼ City Neighbors

◼ Story-Time Neighbors

■ Farm Neighbors

■ Stories We All Like

Illustrations by Louis Cary, Tom Cooke, Cheslie D'Andrea, Ed Gordon, Tom Hill, Hazel Hoecker, Will Huntington, Albert Jousset, Forrest Orr, Catherine Scholz, Dorothy Wagstaff.

We Live Together

Can You Guess?

Mark ran into the house.

"Do you want to see something funny?" he asked Mother.

"Come out and see what we are all playing together."

Mother went out with Mark.
"Look at Joan, Mother," Mark said.
"She is the mother.
The other boys and girls
are her children."

All the children began
to sing this together:
  "There was an old woman
  Who lived in a shoe.
  She had so many children
  She did not know what to do."

A little girl began to sing this
to Joan:
"Oh, Mother, oh, Mother, oh, Mother!
You cannot tell one from the other."

Joan had to guess who said it.
What fun the children had!

Then Joan and Mark's mother
surprised the boys and girls.

She began to sing this to Joan:
"Oh, Mother, oh, Mother, oh, Mother!
You cannot tell one from the other."

"I know who that is," said Kevin.
"So do I," said Kathy.

"Come and play with us, Mother,"
they said.
"I would like to play," said Mother.
"But Daddy will be home soon.
I must get dinner."

Daddy came home.

The children had fun with him.

They asked him to guess
who they were.

Then Daddy and the children
went into the house.

Daddy took Baby Denis
from his little bed.

Daddy and the children went to Mother.

They began to sing this to Mother:
"Here is our family,
One and all;
Here we are, Mother,
Big and small.
Kevin and Kathy,
And Denis too;
Joan and Mark,
And Daddy and you."

The Twins' Birthday Surprise

The twins' birthday had come.
Everyone in the family
said happy birthday to them.
After breakfast Daddy went to work.
Mark and Joan went to school.
So Kevin and Kathy were
at home with Mother and Denis.

Mother began to make
a big birthday cake.
"It will be brown and white,"
she told the twins.

"I know why," said Kathy.
"Kevin likes brown cake.
And I like white cake."

Mother told the twins
to run out and play together.
"We will play a birthday game,"
said Kevin.

The twins went out together.
They saw Mrs. Peters.
They said good morning to her.
Then Kevin said, "Today is
our birthday."
" Well, happy birthday,"
said Mrs. Peters.

Kathy looked up at Mrs. Peters.
"When will the parade come by?"
she asked.
"The parade?" said Mrs. Peters.
"There is no parade today."

"Oh, yes, there is," said the twins.
"But Joan and Mark will not see it.
They went to school today."

Mrs. Green was going to the store.
The twins said good morning to her.
"This is our birthday," said Kathy.

"Well, well," laughed Mrs. Green.
"Two birthdays on the same day!
I know it will be a happy birthday."

"Are you going to the parade?"
asked Kevin.

"What parade?" said Mrs. Green.

"Our birthday parade," Kathy said.

"No one has a birthday parade,"
laughed Mrs. Green.

"Oh, yes, they do," said Kevin.
"There was a big parade
on Mark's birthday."

"When was Mark's birthday?"
asked Mrs. Green.

"On Fire-cracker Day," said Kathy.

Mrs. Green laughed.
"The fire-crackers were not
for Mark's birthday," she said.
"That was not a birthday parade.
Fire-cracker Day is a big day
for everyone."

The twins went into the house.
They looked sad.
"There will not be a parade
for our birthday," they told Mother.

Mother laughed.
"Run out and look for some other
surprise," she said.
"God has put all kinds of surprises
in this world.
See if you can find one."

The twins ran out.
They heard the birds sing.
They saw the green trees.
Down the street they heard
a band playing.

It was a school band playing
for a ball game.

But the twins did not know that.

"Here comes the band," said Kevin.

"Here comes our birthday parade
with a band."

Do Not Walk!

Ted was a little boy.

He lived on the same street
as the twins.

He had just started to school.

Every day he went to school
with Mark and Joan.

They helped him cross the street.

Ted did not like this.

He wanted to be a big boy.

He did not want Mark and Joan
to help him.

One day Ted was going to school with Mark and Joan.

"I am going to cross the street," he said. "I can do it."

And away he ran as fast as he could go.

Mark started to run after Ted. But he could not catch him. Ted ran out into the street. The light was red and said,

Do Not Walk

A bus came up the street.
Cars went up and down the street.
Ted stopped in the street.
He did not know what to do.
"Toot, toot!" went the cars and buses.
Everyone looked at the little boy.

The light told him what to do.
But he was not doing it.
Then a big car came up the street.
The car had a policeman in it.
The policeman jumped out of the car.
He took Ted back to the walk.

The policeman said, "Can't you see that red light, little boy?

It tells you to stop.

Cars may not go on a red light.

Trucks must stop.

The bus man must stop.

They must look at the light.

Little boys must look at it, too.

They must obey the light."

Ted began to grow red.

He did not look at the policeman.

He looked down at his shoes.

After that he looked at the light before he crossed a street.

And he obeyed it.

Traffic Light

We're waiting, and we're waiting,
   And we're looking overhead;
For the traffic light is orange.
   Now we see that it is red!

We're watching, and we're watching,
   And we're patient in between
While we're waiting for the changing
   Of the light from red to green.

We're waiting, and we're staying
   In the place right where we are;
But now the green is showing,
   And my mother starts the car!

Nona Keen Duffy

A Story about the Angels

That night, Mark told Mother
and Daddy about little Ted.

"His angel was with him," said Daddy.
"He took care of Ted."

Then Daddy told the children
this story about the angels.

"Every one of us has
a beautiful angel," he said.

God made the angels before He made
people.

He did not make them like us.

The angels were made to live
in heaven with God.

That is where God wanted to put them.

All the angels were beautiful.

All the angels were happy.

But one day something sad happened.

Some of the angels did not want
to obey God.

So God could not let the bad angels
come into heaven.

He put them in a place
where they cannot see Him.

The bad angels are not beautiful now.
They are not happy.

No one can be happy without God.

The good angels are happy.
They live in heaven with God.
He has made some of them His helpers.
He has given an angel helper
to every one of us.

That angel is with us all the time.
He helps us at work and at play.
He helps us to love and obey God.

Some day our angel will take us
back to God.

If we love and obey God, we will go
to heaven.

There we will see God.

There we will see
all the beautiful angels.

We will live in heaven with them.

Angels

Dear God, I'm sure the angels keep
Their arms around me when I sleep!
For sometimes, when I wake at night
Yes, when my eyes are still shut tight
I hear all sorts of little things
That sound just like an angel's wings!
It wouldn't be a great surprise
If, when I did open my eyes,
I saw an angel by my bed
And touched the halo 'round his head!

Mary Dixon Thayer

A Blue Dog

Have you ever seen a blue dog —
a dog that could run and play?
No one in Mark's family
had ever seen one.
No one on Church Street
had ever seen one.
But one day there was a blue dog
for everyone to see.
This is how it all happened.

Bangs was Mark's pet.
When Mark got him he was not blue.
He was just a brown and white dog.

One morning, Mark said to Joan,
"We must wash Bangs."
Mark got some water.
Bangs jumped into it.
He liked to be washed.
Soon Bangs began to get white.
But he was not as white
as the children wanted him to be.

"I know!" said Joan.

"We can make Bangs very, very white."

"How?" asked Mark.

"Mother has something blue
in the house," said Joan.

"She puts it in the water
when she washes my white dress.

Mother said it makes white things
look whiter."

Mark stopped and looked at Joan.

"That is funny," he said.

"How can blue water make things
look white?"

"You will see," said Joan.

And she ran into the house.

Joan did not tell Mother about Bangs.

She did not ask Mother
for what she wanted.

Soon Joan came back.

"Take Bangs out of the water,"
she said.

Then she began to make the water blue.
Mark put the dog back into the water.
What a surprise he had!
Bangs did not get white.
He got blue.
The children washed and washed
poor Bangs. They tried and tried
to make him white.

But the dog got bluer and bluer.

Daddy called the children.
"Come," he said.
"It is time for dinner."

Bangs heard Daddy, and he
ran away from the children.
Daddy was surprised.
"Why, Bangs!" he said.
"What has happened to you?"

"We have a beautiful dog now,"
said Kathy.
"He looks like my new blue dress."

Mark told Daddy and Mother
what had happened to Bangs.
"You made the water too blue,"
said Daddy.

Mother told the children something, too.
"You must ask to take things
out of the house," she said.
After the children went to bed,
Daddy washed Bangs.
But this time he did not wash him
in blue water.

A Surprise for the Family

Joan was singing as she helped
Mother wash the dishes.

"I can't wait! I can't wait!
It will be fun for all of us."

Mark came into the room.

"Can't wait for what?" he asked.

"Did you forget about the trip?
We are going to take a trip with Daddy,"
said Mother.

"Oh, no," laughed Mark. "I could not
forget the trip. I can't wait to go."

And he began to hop about the room.

"Here comes Daddy now," said Mother.
The children ran to Daddy.
They were so happy to see him.
But he did not look very happy.

"Just one more week to wait, Daddy,"
said Mark. "Just another week before
we go on our trip."

"Are we going far, far away?"
Kevin asked.
"Yes," said Mother. "We will ride
in the car for two days."

"Maybe we can't take that trip now," Daddy said. "It may be a long time before we can go."

Mother looked surprised.

"Can't you get away from your work?" she asked.

"Is our car too old?" asked Mark.

Daddy did not tell Mother and the children what had happened.

He just said they would all pray together.

Then he helped Mother.

They put the children to bed.

After the children were in bed,
Mother and Daddy sat down together.
Then Daddy told Mother something.
He told her why they could not take
the trip.

"I have lost my job," he said.
"I may be out of work for a long time.
So we will have to save our money.
Many other men are out of work, too."

Mother tried not to look sad.
"Oh, my," she said. "That is too bad."
"Shall we tell the children about it?"
Daddy asked Mother.

"Yes," said Mother. "We will tell them.
They can help us to save money.
They can pray that you get another job,
too."

The next morning, Daddy told
the children that he had lost his job.
Then he talked to them
about the trip.

"We cannot go on a trip now,"
he said. "We will have to save
our money. I will look for work.
But it may take a long time."

"Can't we take just a little trip?"
Mark asked.
"Yes," said Daddy. "Maybe next week
we can go to Blue Lake."
"We can all help Daddy now,"
Mother told the children. "You will
be happy with a day at the lake."

"I know how to help you, Daddy," said Mark. "We can do without candy sometimes and save our money."

"I know how to help, too," said Joan. "We can do without shows and save money."

Daddy and Mother looked happy.
"We have a good family," said Daddy. "And that is the best thing of all."

Fun at Blue Lake

The day had come for the trip
to Blue Lake.

"Good-by, Mother. Good-by, Denis,"
said Daddy and the children.

"Have a good time," said Mother.

Daddy and the children talked
about the fun they would have.

Soon they were at Blue Lake.

"See the merry-go-round!" said Joan.
"Look at all the animals on it.
I want to ride on a horse."

"So do I," said Mark. "I want
to ride on this white horse."

"I like elephants," said Kevin.
"I want to ride on a big elephant."
    Daddy got some tickets
for the merry-go-round. He gave them
to the children.
    So Mark rode a beautiful white horse.
    Joan rode a red and green horse.
    Daddy put Kevin on a blue elephant
with yellow ears.
    He put Kathy on a white elephant
with red ears.

44

The merry-go-round started.
All the children began to sing.

"Up, and down, around and around,
See, here we go!
See, here we go!
Up and down, around and around,
See us have fun
On this merry-go-round."

Then the merry-go-round stopped.

After lunch, Daddy took the children
to see the jet planes.

"May Joan and I have a ride
on the jet planes?" Mark asked.

Daddy gave Mark and Joan some money.

"Get your tickets," he told them.
"The twins and I will wait here."

Joan and Mark ran to get the tickets.
The man gave them two tickets.
The children put the money down.
The man did not take the money.

"Look, Joan," said Mark. "The man
gave us two tickets. But he did not take
our money."

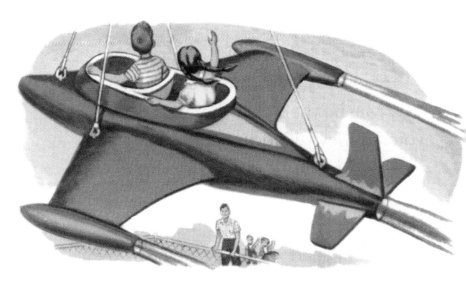

"Now we can get some candy,"
Joan said. "We can have a ride
and candy, too."

The children took the tickets
and the money.

They got into one of the jet planes.
Away they went, up and up and up.

When they looked down, they could
see Daddy and the twins. They looked
very, very small.

Before long, the jets started
to go down. Soon they stopped.
The children got out.

"Look, Daddy," said Mark.
"The ticket man did not take our money."

"Maybe the ticket man did not see your money," Daddy said.

"But we put it down for him to take," Joan said.

"Well, go back and tell the man what happened," said Daddy.

Joan and Mark did not want to take the money back. But they did as they were told.

"I guess I did not see your money," the ticket man said. Then he thanked the children.

Joan and Mark had no candy.
But they had obeyed and were happy.

Have You Heard the News?

"We have some news for you,"
Daddy and Mother told the children.

"What kind of news?" Mark asked.

We are going to move next week,"
said Daddy. "We are going to move
to another house on another street."

"Where is our new house?" asked Joan.
"Is it very far away from here?"

"It is not a new house," said Daddy.
"It is pretty far from here."

"You will see it soon. You
will be surprised," said Mother.
"It is not like this house."

"Oh, I can't wait," said Kathy.
"It must be fun to move."

"Maybe it is fun," said Joan.
"But I would like to have my friends
move, too."

One morning, a big truck came to
help the family move.

Soon everything was out of the house.

Mother, Daddy, and the children
got into the car. They rode a long way.

Then Daddy stopped the car.
"Well, here we are. Hop out,"
he said.
The children looked surprised.
"Is this our new house?"
asked Mark. "What a big house!"
Daddy laughed and said, "Not all
of the house is ours. We shall live
in one part of it. Another family
lives in the other part of the house."
The children looked up and down
the street. They saw many other houses.
They all looked the same.

They saw some stores too. They
did not see any trees and flowers.

"This is not like our other street,"
said Joan. "The houses are big and old.
There are no trees around here."

"We shall plant some flowers here,"
said Mother.

"There is no place to play,"
Mark said.

"Yes, there is a big place to play,"
Daddy said. "There is a playground for
all the children who live around here."

"Oh, good," said Mark.

The family went into the house.

Mark helped Mother and Daddy
put things away.

Joan took care of the twins
and Baby Denis.

That night the family prayed together.
Then Daddy told them something.

"This is our home now," he said.
"The house is not as pretty
as our other one. But this can be
a happy home just the same.

"We will love and help one another.
We will love and obey God. In this way
we shall be happy."

New Neighbors

New House

We've gone to live in a new house
Along a brand new street
Where everything is a new thing
Everything I meet.

There's a new latch on the front gate,
A new bell on the door,
And nothing about the new house
Is as it was before.

We've gone to live in a new house
With a new porch and walk,
And nobody is in the next yard
Who wants to play or talk.

I have to walk in a new park
And climb on a different hill—
Whenever I think of our old house
I wish we lived there still.

Aileen Fisher

Pretty Patches

Joan and Mark soon began to
know their new neighbors. All kinds
of children lived on their street.

Some were big. Some were small.
Some of the children were white.

And some of them were not.

One new friend was named Patches.

Have you ever seen a patch?
Then you can guess why the neighbors
called this little girl Patches.

Poor Patches! She always had holes
in her dresses.

And every time she had a hole,
her mother put a patch over it.

One day, Patches was asked
to a birthday party.

You can't go," her mother said.
"You do not have one good dress.
All your dresses have patches in them."

"Maybe one of my dresses is not
too bad," said Patches.

Mother and Patches walked
into the bedroom.

First they looked at a red dress.
It had a patch.

They looked at a yellow dress. That
had two patches.

Then Mother took out a green dress.
That had three patches on it!

"Oh, my!" said Mother. "All I see
are patches, patches, patches!"

"What about my blue dress, Mother?"
Patches said. "Maybe that would be
a good one for the party."

Mother took out the blue dress.
She showed it to Patches.

"One, two, three, four, five patches!"
laughed Patches. "This dress is the best
of all. I want this one for the party."

"Why, Patches!" said Mother. "You
do not want this dress for the party."

The little girl laughed. "If I
do not have patches on my dress,
the neighbors will not know me," she said.

That night, after Patches was in bed,
Mother began to work on the blue dress.

First she cut out a yellow duck
and put it over one patch.

Then she cut out a white bunny
and put it over another patch.

Over the other three patches
Mother put a horse, a squirrel,
and an elephant.

Then she put the blue dress
in Patches' room. Patches would see it
the first thing in the morning.

The next morning, Patches saw
the surprise. She jumped out of bed.

"Oh, come, Mother," she called.
"See what has happened to my blue dress.
A fairy must have come here last night."

Mother laughed. "There is
a kind fairy like that in every home,"
she said.

That day, Patches went
to the birthday party.

"Look at the pretty new dress
Patches has!" said her friends.

"This is my old blue dress," Patches
told them. "Last night a fairy came
and put these little animals on it."

"A real fairy?" asked the children.

"Yes, a real fairy," said Patches.
"My mother told me that there is
a fairy like that in every home."

Do you know who the fairy is?

The Boy Who Could Not Forget

Joan and Mark had many good times with their new friends.

One day, some of the children were going to a show. Mark wanted to go, too.

"Please, Daddy, let me go," said Mark. "All my friends are going to the show. I want to go, too."

"It is not the kind of show for you to see," Daddy said. "You may see a good show, but not that one."

"All the other children on our street can go," Mark said. "They are all good boys and girls. I play with them every day."

"You must not do things just because other people do them," said Daddy. "All the children on this street may go to the show. But that cannot make it good.

"Do you want to do something that is not right?"

Mark loved Daddy and liked to obey him. He liked to do as he was told. But today he did not feel that way.

Mark wanted to do what his friends did. He wanted to go to the show.

Daddy said good-by to the family.
This was his first day at work.
He was happy to have a new job.

Mother was working in another part
of the house.

Joan was out playing with the twins.

Mark sat down to look at TV.
He heard the telephone ring. It was
one of the neighbor boys.

"Hello, Mark," said the boy.
"Are you going to the show with us?"

"No, my father will not let me go,"
said Mark. "He said the show is not
a good one for me to see."

"But we are all going. It must be
all right," the boy said.

"No, I guess I can't go," Mark told his friend.

"I will pay for your ticket," the boy told Mark. "You will not have to let your father know about it. Will you go?"

Mark looked around. There was no one in the room.

"All right," he said. "That show cannot hurt me. I will come over to your house right away."

Away Mark ran as fast as he could. But he did not feel very happy.

He could not forget what his father had said.

There were many people at the show.

The big boy took out his money. He was going to pay for Mark.

He looked down to say something to Mark. But Mark was not there.

No one saw what had happened. No one but God.

Mark had run back home. He did not want to go to the show now.

He could not forget what his father had told him.

The Twins Play a Game

One day, Mother gave Kathy and Kevin a box of cards to play with. There were all kinds of cards in the box.

Some were birthday cards.

Some were get-well cards.

Some were name cards.

The twins looked at all the cards.

Kevin said, "We can play a game. We will go to the houses on our street. We will put a card in every mailbox."

"All right," said Kathy. "That will be fun."

So away the twins ran.

They stopped at Mrs. Lake's house.
She was not at home. That was good.

Mrs. Lake was a very cross woman.

She did not like Kevin and Kathy's
family. She never talked to their mother
and father.

But the twins did not know that.

Kevin took out a white card
with Mother's name on it. He put it
into Mrs. Lake's mailbox.

Then he and Kathy went
to the next house.

Miss Long lived in the next house.
Today was her birthday. No one
ever thought of Miss Long's birthday.
She never got birthday cards.

Kathy and Kevin did not know
about her birthday. She was always kind
to them. And they liked her.

They looked for the best card
in their box. Guess what it was?
A beautiful birthday card! They put it
into Miss Long's mailbox.

Miss Long came home from work. She found the card in her mailbox.

"This cannot be for me," she thought.

Then she looked at the card. "It is for me! Someone did not forget my birthday!" she said.

There was no name on the card.

Miss Long did not know who put it in her mailbox. But she was happy that someone had thought of her birthday.

The twins stopped at five other houses. Then they began to feel tired.

Now they had only get-well cards in the box.

They went by Mr. Hill's house. He
was not well.

He was sleeping in his big chair.
The twins put all the get-well cards
by the chair.

What a surprise Mr. Hill had
when he found all the cards!

"What good friends I have!" he said.
"They all came to see me today,
and I was sleeping."

That night after dinner, the twins' family had a big surprise.

Mrs. Lake, the cross woman, came to the house. But she did not look cross now.

She smiled at Mother. She was very happy.

"Thank you for coming to see me," she said. "We shall be good friends."

Mother did not know what Mrs. Lake was talking about. She did not know about the name card in the mailbox. But she was very happy to see Mrs. Lake smile.

And from that day on, Mrs. Lake and the twins' family were good friends.

The Robber Family

One day Bob ran to Mark's house.

"I have some news for you," he said.
"A new family has just moved
to our street. And the people are
very bad. They are robbers!

"My mother heard a neighbor talking.
She heard her say that they are robbers.
They have a boy as old as we are."

"I do not want to play with a robber,"
Mark said. "Do you?"

"No," said Bob. "The robber boy
would take our money and toys."

For three weeks, the robber boy had no one to play with.

He tried to make friends with the neighbor children. But they always ran away from him.

Some of the boys and girls would not even walk by his house.

Some children would cross the street. Then they would not even have to be near the robber family's house.

One day, Bob and his mother were out in their car. Just as they came
to the robber family's house, the car stopped.

Bob's mother tried and tried. But she could not start the car.

The robber boy and his father came out of their house. They asked if they could help.

The robber boy's mother asked Bob's mother to come into the house.

The robber boy's father worked on the car. The two boys helped him. Soon it began to run again.

"Thank you for your help," said Bob's mother.

"Thank you," said the robber boy's mother. "This has been a very happy day for us."

That day, Bob and his mother found out the name of their neighbors. They were Mr. and Mrs. Robber. The boy's name was Bill Robber.

They found out, too, what kind people the Robbers were.

The next day Bob went out to play ball with his friends. And with him was Bill Robber.

Some of the boys saw the Robber boy. They began to walk away. Bob called them back.

"This is Bill, and his last name is Robber," Bob told his friends. "He is not a robber just because of his name. My last name is Farmer. But no one in my family is a real farmer."

"I know a family by the name of Green," laughed Mark. "But the people in that family are not green."

"How funny!" said Bob. "And that is why we did not want Bill to play with us."

After that, Bill Robber was one of the best-liked boys on the street.

And Mr. and Mrs. Robber found many new friends, too.

Uncle Tim

Joan and Mark had helped their father to plant seeds in boxes.

Every day, the two children watered the plants and took care of them.

Then they waited for a surprise. And one morning they found it.

There were pretty flowers in two of the boxes.

That day, Joan said to Mark, "I would like to give some of these flowers to Uncle Tim Hill. He never gets out of his house to see pretty flowers."

Mr. Hill was not a real uncle.
All the children on the street called
him Uncle Tim because he was so kind
to children.

He liked to make them happy. He
always told the best stories.

Uncle Tim could not work. He had
hurt his leg and could not walk.
He had no one to take care of him.

After school, Joan and Mark took some of their flowers to Uncle Tim.

"Hello, Uncle Tim," they said. "See what we have for you today."

"We helped Daddy plant these when we moved here," said Mark.

"These pretty flowers will make you feel better," Joan said.

"What beautiful flowers!" said Uncle Tim. "How kind of you to think of me."

Then Uncle Tim told the children something.

"These flowers make me think
of the time when I was a little boy,"
he said.

"We had flowers just like these
around our house. Sometimes I took them
to church for the altar.

"I loved God then and I was happy.
But when I got to be a man, I did
not think about Him.

"I stopped going to church. I did not
take time to pray. Now I do not
even know the Our Father."

The two children looked surprised.

"You do not know how to pray?" said Mark. "You do not know how to say the Our Father?"

"Even our little twins can pray," Joan said. "Our family prays together every night."

"Maybe we could help you to pray again," Mark said.

Uncle Tim began to smile.

"I would be very happy to have you help me," he said. "You have helped me today.

"These flowers have made me think of the things that I tried to forget."

The very next day, Mark and Joan
went again to Uncle Tim's house.
They showed him how to pray.

After that, they went to see him
every week.

Soon Uncle Tim began to feel better.
He started to go to church again.
He prayed every day.

When he was a little boy, he had
been happy. And now he was happy
again.

The Wise Little Owl

Uncle Tim told the children
many stories. This is one of the stories
they liked the best.

Little Brown Owl sat up in a tree.

"Who-oo! Who-oo!" he said. Owls
are wise, they say. But poor me! I am
not wise. What shall I do?"

Little Owl looked all around.

Then he said, "I know. I will go
to see the little old man who lives
over the hill. Maybe he can tell me
how to be wise."

And away Little Owl went, as fast
as he could go.

Little Brown Owl flew over the hill.

The old man saw him and said,
"Go away, Brown Owl! This is a bad day.

My legs hurt. Everything hurts. I think
that it is going to rain."

So Little Brown Owl flew away.

"Maybe the little old woman who lives
near the lake can help me," he said.

He went to the old woman's house.
She was just going out.

"Do not come to see me today,"
she said. "My best friend is sick.
I am going to get some seeds
that will make her better."

"Good-by," said Little Brown Owl
and he flew away.

Little Brown Owl saw the farmer.
He had on his big sun hat.

"I have no time for you today,"
he said. "I have work to do. I want
to pick some apples for my family."

Poor Little Brown Owl went away.

"No one has any time for me today.
I guess I shall never know how to be
wise like other owls," he said.

As Little Brown Owl was going home,
he met Mrs. Rabbit.

"Hello, Brown Owl," she said. "I am
going to have a party today. Would
you like to come?"

"Oh, yes," said Brown Owl. "But I think it is going to rain today."

"My! What a wise owl you are!" said Mrs. Rabbit. "I shall have my party some other day."

Next Brown Owl met Mrs. Hen. She was crying.

"Cluck, cluck! One of my chicks is sick," she cried. "I do not know what to give her."

"Go to the little old woman who lives near the lake. She has some kind of seeds that make sick people better," said Brown Owl.

"What a wise little owl you are!" said Mrs. Hen and she went away.

At the top of the hill, Brown Owl met Mrs. Squirrel.

"I just do not know what to do," she said. "I told my children they would have a surprise for lunch today. Now I can't think of one thing to have."

"There are apples on the tree near the farmer's house," said Brown Owl. "You could pick some for an apple pie for your children."

"My, but you are a wise little owl," smiled Mrs. Squirrel. "I shall get some apples right away."

Then Little Brown Owl flew home. He sat up in the tree for a long time.

"Mrs. Rabbit said I was a wise little owl," he said. "Mrs. Squirrel and Mrs. Hen think that I am very wise."

Then Little Brown Owl began to smile.

"Who-oo! who-oo!" he cried. "I guess I am a real owl. I guess I am just as wise as all the other owls!"

School Neighbors

A Trip to the Library

Betty and Peter lived on the same street as Mark and Joan. They were all good friends. They all went to Saint Mary's School.

One day, the children in Mark's room were to go to the library. They were going by bus.

"We had better run if we want to be on time for the bus," said Mark.

"Oh, I do not want to miss it," said Betty. "I want to get a library card. Then I can take books home to read."

"Here comes Joseph," said Peter. "Let's wait for him."

"Run, Joseph, run!" cried the children.

Joseph began to run. But he ran too fast. Down he went!

"Oh, my leg!" he cried. "I have hurt my leg."

Betty and Mark looked at Peter. They knew they could not wait for Joseph. If they did, they would miss the bus.

Then Peter said to Mark, "You and Betty go on. I will help Joseph."

"But you will miss the trip
to the library," said Betty. "We must be
in the bus by one o'clock."

"Please go on," said Peter. "I will
help Joseph."

Mark and Betty ran to school.
They got there just in time to get
into the bus. They told Sister Ann
about Peter and Joseph.

"It is too bad that the boys cannot be
with us," she said. "But I am happy
that Peter helped Joseph."

At the library the children saw
many kinds of books.

There were books about flowers, trees,
and plants.

There were animal books.

Some books were about jet planes,
boats, and trucks.

There were books about God
and the angels.

There were books about everything.
"I never knew there were so many
kinds of books," said one of the boys.

Miss Brooks worked in the library.
She took the children to all the rooms.

She showed them all kinds of books.
She showed the children how to get
their library cards.

Then she and Sister Ann helped
the children find books. The children
wanted to take out all kinds of books.

Betty took out two books
on her library card. One was for herself,
and the other book was for Peter.

Mark took out three books
on his library card. He had a book
for himself, and a book for Joseph, and
a book for Peter.

The other children did not know
about the books that Mark and Betty had.
Every boy and girl took out books
for Joseph and Peter.

The next day the children ran
to Peter and Joseph.

"See what we have for you," they said.

Then they gave the books
to Joseph and Peter.

"Look at us!" cried Peter. "We
did not go to the library. But we have
more books than anyone!"

Story Time in School

One day, Sister Ann told the children about something new they would do.

"Once every week, we will have story time in this room," she said. "You may read stories from your library books to the other children."

That week, Peter was asked to read from one of his library books.

This is the story he liked better than any other.

The Long Trip

Jesus, Mary, and Saint Joseph
are our friends in heaven.

They once lived here in this world
just as we do.

Jesus is the Son of God, but He came
from heaven to help us. He came
as a little baby.

Mother Mary and Saint Joseph made
a little home for Him. But Jesus, Mary,
and Saint Joseph did not live there long.

Something happened.

One night, little Jesus, Mother Mary,
and Saint Joseph were sleeping. It was
very dark.

All at once Saint Joseph heard someone say, "Get up, Joseph. Take little Jesus and Mother Mary away.

"A bad king is looking for a baby who is to be a King. He may find Baby Jesus. You must go away."

Saint Joseph knew that this was one of God's beautiful angels.

God must have told the angel what to say to him.

But Saint Joseph did not know where to go with Jesus and Mary.

Then the beautiful angel said, "Go to another land far, far away from here."

And the angel told Saint Joseph the name of the land.

Saint Joseph must have been tired. He had worked all day. He may even have wanted to go back to sleep. But he did not do that.

Saint Joseph got up at once.

"I will do as God wants," he said to himself.

Then he called Mother Mary. He told her what had happened.

Mary and Saint Joseph must have been sad to go away from their little home. But they obeyed God.

They took little Jesus and began their long trip to the far-away land.

For a long time, Jesus, Mary, and Saint Joseph lived in that land far away.

The bad king died. Then God's angel came again to Saint Joseph.

This time the angel told Saint Joseph that he could take Baby Jesus and Mother Mary back to their own home.

So Jesus, Mary, and Saint Joseph went to the home that they loved so well.

Jesus lived with Mother Mary
and Saint Joseph for a long time.
He did all that His Father
in heaven wanted Him to do.
He worked and played and prayed.
He was kind to others.
He loved His mother and Saint Joseph.
He did everything they told Him to do.
Jesus did all of these things to show
us how to be good boys and girls.

How Mary Saved Her Father

Sister Ann asked Joseph to read
this story from one of his library books.

There was once a girl who lived
in a lighthouse with her father.

Her name was Mary.

Mary had no mother. Her friends
lived over in the city.

Sometimes Mary played with big white
birds that came in from the water.

Sometimes she went out in the boat
with her father.

Mary knew all about boats,
just as boys and girls today know
about cars and planes.

Every day, when it began to get dark, Mary and her father went to the top of the lighthouse.

There her father put on the big light.

Her father said, "There are many men out in their boats. They would get lost if the big light were not on."

At night, Mary liked to go out and look up at the stars. She called them the lights in God's big lighthouse.

Mary would laugh and say, "See, Father! The angels did not forget to put on the lights!"

One morning, Mary's father said,
"I must go over to the city today.
I shall be back as soon as I can."

Mary said good-by to her father.
Then she began to make the beds
and to wash the breakfast dishes.

Just then, Mary heard something.
"That is the wind," she said. It is
going to rain before Father gets home."

Soon the sky began to grow black.

Mary waited and waited. One o'clock
came. Two o'clock came. Three o'clock
came, and Mary's father was not home.

Then Mary thought of the light
on top of the lighthouse.

She knew that men were out
in their boats. They would look
for the light on a dark day like this.

Mary went to the top of the lighthouse.
But she could not reach the light.

Then she thought of the chair
in her father's room. She got up
on the chair. At last she could reach
the light and put it on.

As Mary waited for her father to come
home, she prayed, "Oh, please, dear God,
help my father. Do not let anything
happen to him."

At five o'clock, the door opened.
The wind and rain came into the room.
There at last was Mary's father!

"Oh, Father!" Mary cried. "I prayed
you would come soon."

Then Mary and her father went
into the next room. There,
before a small altar, they thanked God
for helping them.

That night, Father told Mary
about his trip.

"I started home after lunch," he said.
It started raining, and the wind began
to blow. The sky was very black.

"I thought I had lost my way.
Then I saw the light on top
of the lighthouse."

How happy Mary was that she
had thought of the light! She
had saved her own father.

Name the Worker

Miss Green taught the boys and girls in Room Two at Saint Joseph's School.

One day it was raining. The children could not go out to play.

Miss Green said, "Let's think of names. Think of all the people who helped us in some way today."

Tom began the game. "God helped us," he said. "Without Him, we can't do anything."

"That is right," said Miss Green. "Now let's think of the people who helped us and worked for us today."

Jean was next. She said, "My mother called me this morning and fixed my breakfast for me."

"My mother gave me a good lunch and fixed my hair," said Ann.

Jim was next. He said, "It was raining this morning. So my father gave me a ride in his car."

"The bus man helped me," said Ted. "I came to school in the bus today."

"Mr. Singer, the policeman, helped us
to cross the street. He saw that
we did not get hurt," said Bill.

"Someone is helping me right now,"
said Tom. "A man is at our house.
He is painting my bedroom."

"The TV man is coming to our house
after school," said Pete. "He is
going to fix our TV. Then we can see
Story Parade at five o'clock."

"Father Brown helped all of us,"
said Jim. "He said Mass this morning."

"You helped us, Miss Green,"
said Bobby. "You taught us about God.
You taught us how to read. You taught us
many things today."

"Thank you," said Miss Green. Then
she looked at Marie. "Did anyone
help you today, Marie?" she asked.

"Well, I guess Doctor Best did, but he hurt me a little, too," said Marie.

Miss Green laughed. "Doctor Best is your friend. He did not want to hurt you," she said. "Sometimes doctors have to hurt you to help you."

"I know someone who helps us," said David. "The farmer takes care of the land and grows our food."

Soon it was time for school to start again. The children had to stop their game. They took out their books and papers.

"I never knew so many people worked for us," said Marie.

"We have named only some helpers," said Miss Green. "Just think of all the people who make our clothes.

"We need people to put up houses and schools and churches.

"We need people to work in stores. We need people to run planes, trucks, boats, and buses.

"We, too, can help other people. We all need other people."

The Dog's Dark Days

When his TV was fixed, Pete saw and heard this story.

There was once a dog that found some dark glasses down by the lake. He picked them up and put them on.

Then he started off to show his friends. But the glasses made everything around him look very dark.

"I had better go home right away," he said. "It looks like rain. It may rain before I get home."

The dog started to run. He ran as fast as his four legs would go.

On the way the dog met his friend, the horse.

"You had better get into the barn," said the dog to the horse. "Just look at that dark sky. It is going to rain before long."

"How funny for you to say that! The sun is out," said the horse. "It will never rain on a beautiful day like this."

The horse walked on with his wagon. And the dog looked up at the sky again.

"That is funny," he said. "Maybe it is night time. That is why it is so dark."

So the dog sat down and went to sleep.

Soon Betty Bunny came by and saw the dog.

"How can you sleep at this time of the day?" she said.

"This is the right time to sleep," said the dog. "What are you doing out in the dark?"

"Out in the dark!" cried Betty Bunny. "Why, the sun is out, and the sky is blue. What a silly dog!"

Betty Bunny ran on to get her lunch.

Then the dog saw White Cat coming down the hill. Now White Cat's coat was always just as white as it could be. The dog looked and looked at her.

"White Cat, what has happened to your coat?" he asked. "I have never seen you look like that! You had better go home and get washed. Your friends may see you."

"You are talking silly," said White Cat, as she looked at her pretty white coat.

"Mew, mew! I shall fix you!" she cried and jumped at the dog.

The dog began to run after the cat. He ran so fast that his dark glasses came off.

How surprised he was when he saw White Cat up in the tree! Her coat was just as clean as it had always been!

The poor dog walked home. The sky was blue. The sun was out. It did not look like rain.

"I shall never, never again put on dark glasses," he said.

And he never did.

My Literary Dog

My puppy wants to read my books,
    He acts so very wise;
He wags his tail and looks and looks;
    I think he really tries.
He cocks his head a funny way;
    He tries his best to see
And then he begs, as if to say,
    "Now, won't you read to me!"

Elise de Saint Andre

City Neighbors

Garden Surprises

Mr. Bird had a seed store in the city.

One day he lost his glasses. He could not see what he was doing.

All day long he put seeds into little bags. But poor Mr. Bird could not read the names on the bags.

He did not know if the right kinds of seeds were going into the right bags. Mr. Bird did not even care. This was the sad part.

"Seeds are seeds," he said to himself. "They will all grow to be something."

Soon it was time for people to plant their gardens.

Mr. Bird's seed store had always been the best one in the city. Everyone went there to get seeds.

Seeds for beans. Seeds for all kinds of flowers. Seeds for just about anything you could plant!

Things went well for about five weeks.

Then one evening the door opened. In came Mr. Black. He was not happy.

"Look here, Mr. Bird," said Mr. Black. "The flower seeds you gave me are not flower seeds at all. They are coming up in my garden as yellow beans. My family will not eat yellow beans!"

The next day Doctor King called on the telephone.

"Oh, Mr. Bird!" said the doctor. "The bean seeds I got from you are coming up as carrots. Now I have too many carrots. I do not know what to do with them."

Soon after that the door opened again. In came Mrs. Bee.

"I do not like to tell you this, Mr. Bird," she said. "But the seeds I got for my garden should have been carrots.

"They are not carrots. They are coming up as four o'clocks. My family can't eat flowers for carrots."

One after another, the people came to the seed store. They told what had happened in their gardens.

Mr. Bird did not feel at all happy about this.

Then one day Mr. Bird had a thought.
That evening, he was on TV.

"My seed store will give a prize,"
Mr. Bird said. "The one who has found
the funniest surprise in his garden
will get the prize."

The next day, Mr. Black took
yellow beans to the store. They
should have been flowers.

Doctor King came to show the carrots
that should have been beans.

Mrs. Bee came with four o'clocks
that should have been carrots.

But Mrs. Horn had the funniest surprise
of all. Her two boys walked
into the store with a big box.

"These should have been little forget-me-not plants," laughed Mrs. Horn. "But just look! See what they are!"

In the box were two big pumpkins!

Everyone in the store began to laugh. They thought it was very funny.

"Well, that takes the prize," said Mr. Bird.

And he gave Mrs. Horn the prize. It was a box of beautiful new dishes.

From that day, Mr. Bird never lost his glasses again. And the right seeds always got into the right bags.

The Hacker-Crackers' Busy Day

Every day was a busy one
for Mrs. Hacker-Cracker. But this day
all the children were home from school.

The Hacker-Cracker family was
a very big one. There were Daddy
Hacker-Cracker, Mother Hacker-Cracker,
and many little Hacker-Crackers.
Five boys and five girls.

Mother Hacker-Cracker was busy doing
her work. Then she thought of something.

"Oh, my!" she said to the children.
"This is your father's birthday. We
must make a cake for him."

Mother Hacker-Cracker got out three eggs and some milk. Then she went to get some butter.

"No butter!" she said. "Who ate all the butter? We can't make a cake without butter. Come, we shall all go to the store and get some butter."

"All of us? Must we all go?" asked one of the boys. "Uncle Bill will not like that."

"Every last one of us," said Mother.

So the big Hacker-Crackers and the little Hacker-Crackers walked down the street to Uncle Bill's store.

"What do you all want in this store?" Uncle Bill asked when he saw the family.

"Butter for a birthday cake," said all the little Hacker-Crackers.

"Birthday cake! Who has a birthday?" he asked.

"Daddy Hacker-Cracker," said one of the boys.

"Who wants an old birthday cake? No one ever gave me a birthday cake," said Uncle Bill.

One of the little Hacker-Crackers looked at Mother and said something. No one but Mother heard.

"I will take two boxes of butter," Mother told Uncle Bill.

Uncle Bill looked very cross. All the little Hacker-Crackers tried not to be seen. They were happy to get out of their uncle's store. And they ran all the way home.

That day Mother Hacker-Cracker made two birthday cakes.

"This one is for your father," she told the children. "And this one is for your Uncle Bill."

"A cake for Uncle Bill!" said one of the boys.

"Uncle Bill!" said all the rest of the family.

"Yes, for Uncle Bill," said Mother. "We must be kind to him. Uncle Bill is not as cross as he looks. Maybe this cake will be good for him."

That evening, the Hacker-Cracker family had a big party at their house.

They had ice cream with the cakes. All the Hacker-Crackers liked ice cream very much.

Uncle Bill was there. He saw the two beautiful birthday cakes. He was happy as he could be.

His cake had pretty flowers on it. He just could not stop looking at it.

"I always wanted a cake like that," he said. "But no one ever gave me one."

After that, Uncle Bill was always as kind and as happy as he could be.

The Little Soldier

Tom jumped out of bed. How happy he was when he looked out!

First of all, the sun was out. It was a beautiful day.

Then there were the flags. Tom could see a red, white, and blue flag on every house on his street.

Best of all, today there would be a parade! The City Band was going to play.

Yes, this was going to be a big day for everyone!

Tom put on his clean new clothes and ate his breakfast as fast as he could. Then he ran over to Jim's house.

"Look at me," Tom said to his friend. "Do I look like a real soldier?"

"Yes," said Jim. "But look at what I have for the parade!"

And Jim showed Tom his new flag.

Just then the boys heard something.

"The band! The band!" said Tom. "Let's go. The parade is starting."

The two boys ran from Jim's house.
Jim took his flag and ran down the street.
But Tom had to go home first. He
wanted to get his soldier hat and boots.

After he got his hat and boots, Tom
started after Jim. But he did not get
very far.

On the next street, he saw
a little black dog. The dog had been hurt.
Tom stopped and looked at the dog.

"You poor little dog," he said.
"Don't cry. I will help you."

So Tom picked up the dog and started
for home.

"Well, I guess I will not be
in the parade today," he said.

"I wanted to see the soldiers.
I wanted to be in the parade with them,
too. But, more than that, I want
to help you, little dog."

Just then, Tom heard someone say,
"You are a real soldier."

Tom looked up and saw a real soldier.
On the soldier's coat was a little
gold pin. How pretty the pin looked
in the sunlight!

The soldier said, "Have you ever seen a pin like this? I got this for helping a friend who was hurt.

"It is fun to be in parades. But that will not make you a real soldier. A real soldier helps other people."

The soldier took the gold pin from his coat. He gave it to Tom.

"Now you are a real soldier, too," he said.

Tom ran home as fast as he could go. He told Mother and Daddy about the dog and the soldier. He showed them his gold pin. He called it his prize.

Mother helped Tom to take care of the dog. That night, Tom thanked God for the beautiful day. And he took the gold pin to bed with him!

Run-Away Tom-Tom

Poor Mr. Gabriel did not know what to do. He ran up and down the street. He looked here, there, and everywhere.

"Where are you, Tom-Tom?" he called. "Oh, where are you?"

Joan and Mark and some of the other children were coming home from school. When they heard Mr. Gabriel, they started looking all around.

The children knew Tom-Tom. He was the funny little monkey in Mr. Gabriel's pet store.

"Tom-Tom has run away," Mr. Gabriel told the children.

"There he is!" cried Bob. "He is jumping off the top of that house!"

Tom-Tom jumped fast and far. He looked as if he were flying.

"Now he is in the tree!" cried Joan.

Mr. Gabriel took off his hat. He waved it to the monkey. "Will you come down, Tom-Tom?" he called.

The little monkey looked down at Mr. Gabriel and the children. He took off his own little hat and waved back to him.

How the children laughed at the little monkey!

"Oh, please come down, Tom-Tom,"
Mr. Gabriel said. "I should be back
in my store. No one is there to
take care of things."

Just then, Mary, a new girl at school,
came by. "I think my daddy can come
and help you," she told Mr. Gabriel.

"But, Mary," said Bob. "Your father
can't come here now. He is at work."

Mary had not heard what Bob said.
She had run off down the street.

"I do not think her father can come
here now," said Joan. "Let's try to get
Tom-Tom down from that tree."

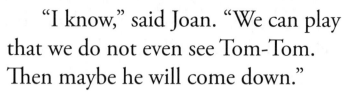

"I know," said Joan. "We can play that we do not even see Tom-Tom. Then maybe he will come down."

The children sat down. They all turned their backs to Tom-Tom.

The monkey sat in the tree and did the same thing. He turned his back to the children.

"Oh, dear! He does just what we do," said Mark. "But he will not come down."

Just then the children heard a clang,
clang! It was a big red fire truck.
In the fire truck sat Mary.

"My daddy will help us get Tom-Tom,"
said Mary. "He is a fireman."

Mary's father and another fireman
looked at the monkey up in the tree.

"We will get him down," they said.

Mary's father went up into the tree.
He talked to the monkey. Then he
took off his hat and put it on the tree.

Tom-Tom put his hat on the tree, too.

The monkey looked down and waved at the children. He knew they would laugh. He was right.

They laughed and laughed. So Tom-Tom went right on showing off.

Mary's father thought of something. He put some nuts into his hand. He put his hand near the monkey.

Tom-Tom moved over and began to eat the nuts. Down came the fireman's hand! Tom-Tom could not get away this time.

"Good work!" cried the children.

"How shall I ever thank you?" said Mr. Gabriel. "It was kind of you to come here and help me."

"We are always happy to help," said the fireman. "But we must get back to the firehouse now. There may be a fire somewhere."

"Now I know that a fireman does more than put out fires," said Bob.

"Yes," said Mary's father. "We try to help in as many ways as we can."

"Thank you, thank you," called the children.

They waved good-by as the fire truck went down the street. Tom-Tom was busy eating nuts. But he saw the children wave, and he did the same thing. He waved, too.

Mary Ann Gets a Hair Cut

Mrs. Flag put some money
into Mary Ann's coat pocket.

"Run down to Mr. Cook," she said.
"He will cut your hair. But you must be
there by two o'clock. Tell him to cut it
just up to your ears and no more.

"Now, take care of your money,
Mary Ann. Hurry back home
after your hair has been cut."

Mary Ann said good-by to her mother,
and off she went down the street.

On her way, Mary Ann met her best friend, Pam.

"I am going to get my hair cut," she told Pam. "Do you want to come with me?"

Mary Ann showed Pam the money in her pocket.

"That is so much money to pay for a hair cut," said Pam. "Just think of all the ice cream and candy we could get with that many dimes!"

Then Pam thought of something. She said, "My mother cuts my hair. I think I could cut yours, Mary Ann. We could save the money. Then we could get some ice cream with it."

"All right, let's do it," said Mary Ann.

The two girls went into Pam's house. They went into her bedroom.

Mary Ann sat down on a small chair. Pam started to cut her hair.

"Don't forget," said Mary Ann. "Only up to my ears!"

"Zip-zip, zip-zip, zip-zip!" Pam cut this way and that way. She cut one side. Then she cut the other side.

"Hurry up, Pam," said Mary Ann. "You are so slow. Mr. Cook never takes so long to cut my hair."

"One side is not even with the other," said Pam. "I shall cut off just a little more on this side. Then you will look all right."

"Please hurry, Pam," said Mary Ann.
"My ears feel cold." Mary Ann put her
hand up to feel her hair.

"Oh, Pam," she cried, "what did you
do to my hair? I think you cut it all
off." Then Mary Ann cried and cried.

"Oh, dear!" said Pam, "I should never
have tried to cut your hair. It looks
silly. What will your mother say?
Will she punish you?"

Pam went home with Mary Ann.

"I was the one who wanted to get
ice cream and candy with your money,"
she said. "So I will tell your mother."

Mrs. Flag looked at Mary Ann.
She did not know her at first. Then
she looked again.

"Good heavens!" she cried. "What
has happened to your hair?"

The girls told Mother.

"You did not do as you were told,"
Mary Ann's mother said. "I should
punish you. But I will not have to.

"The looking glass will take care
of that. It will punish you every time
you look into it."

Mary Ann saw herself in the
looking glass and began to cry.

"Mother," she cried. "What can I do?"

You can't do anything now,"
said Mother. "You can only wait
for your hair to grow and be pretty
again."

The next day, Mary Ann did not take
off her hat in school.

"Why, Mary Ann!" said everyone
in her room. "Why do you have a hat on
in school?"

Then Mary Ann showed the children
what had happened because she had not
obeyed her mother.

At the Barber's Shop

I love to go to the barber's shop
    And sit in his great, high chair.
The scissors go snappity-snippity-snap
    As the barber cuts my hair.

The electric clippers buzz and buzz
    Like a million honeybees.
And the chair can whirl like a
        merry-go-round
    If the barber and captain please.
Then the barber brushes my clothes
        so clean
    As I slide from the great, high chair,
And skippity-hoppity home I go,
    With only half my hair.

Bette Killion

Story-Time Neighbors

The Old Woman and the New Bird

There was once a little old woman. She lived in a pretty little house.

She had no friends, and children never went to her house.

One morning, the little old woman got up. She put on a black dress, a clean white apron, and a little red cap.

"This would be a good day to make cakes," she said.

Now this little old woman liked to make cakes, cookies, and buns.

She made very good ones, but she would not give them away. She ate every one she made.

The little old woman began to work.
Soon an old man came to the door.

"I am very hungry," he said.
"I have walked far. I have had no food
for a long time. Could you give me
one of your cakes?"

The old woman looked at the man.
Then she looked at the brown cakes.

"These cakes are too big
to give away," she thought. "I will make
a little cake for the poor man."

So she told the man to wait.
And she started to make a cake for him.

The little old woman tried to make
a small cake. But the cake was as big
as the others.

"This cake is too big," she thought.
"I will make a wee little cake."

So she put a wee cake into a pan.
The wee cake began to get big. Soon
it was very, very big.

The old woman would not give it away.

"Just wait," she told the poor man.
"You will get some kind of a cake."

This time, the old woman tried to make
a wee, wee cake. Just as small as it
could be.

But that cake, too, was very, very big
when she took it out of the pan.

At last the little old woman went
to the man. "Take this bread," she said.
"I have no cakes for you."

The hungry man thanked the woman.
He said, "I have no money to give you
for this bread. But you may wish
for anything you want and you shall
have it."

With that the old man walked away.
He looked very old and tired.

The old woman thought, "I should
have given him something better to eat.

"I wish I were a bird. I would fly
after him. I would fly very fast and
give him one of my big brown cakes."

The little old woman had just said
this when something happened.

She looked down at her hands.
They were wings! Now she was not
a little old woman. She was a bird!

She had on her black dress, her clean
white apron, and her little red cap.
But they did not look the same.

Then the wind began to blow. It took
the old woman out of the doorway
to the top of a big tree.

Have you ever seen a bird that looks
like the little old woman? The bird
is black and white with a red cap.

Do you know this bird's name?

Mrs. Goose and the Rain

Mrs. Goose was busy washing
her lunch dishes. It was raining outside,
so Mrs. Goose sang about the rain.

All at once she heard something.
It came from the bedroom. Mrs. Goose
went to see what it was.

"Oh, my! Oh, my!" she said
to herself. "It is raining right
into my bedroom. I must get Mr. Goat
to come over at once!"

Mrs. Goose put a flower pot and
a dish pan near the bed to catch the rain.

Then she put on her raincoat and
started off for Mr. Goat's house.

Mr. Goat was eating lunch
when Mrs. Goose got to his house.

"What are you doing out in the rain?"
he asked her.

"Oh, please come over to my house
right away," said Mrs. Goose. "I want
you to fix my roof."

"It is raining too much. I can't fix the roof now," said Mr. Goat. "I must wait for the rain to stop."

"All right," said Mrs. Goose. "Come tomorrow, please."

The next day the sun was out. Mr. Goat called Mrs. Goose on the telephone.

"I will be right over to fix the roof of your house," he told her.

"But it is not raining in my house today," said Mrs. Goose. "It would be silly for you to come now."

So Mr. Goat did not go to Mrs. Goose's house that day.

The very next night, it started
to rain again. The rain was coming down
right on Mrs. Goose's bed.

She jumped out of bed and turned on
the light. She went to the telephone
and called Mr. Goat.

"You must come at once," she told
him. "It is raining in again. I can't
sleep. The rain is coming down
on top of my bed."

"I can't fix your roof at night,"
said Mr. Goat. "I can't fix it
in the rain. I will be there tomorrow
if it is not raining."

The next morning, Mr. Goat went to Mrs. Goose's house to fix the roof.

"Does the rain come in all over your house?" he asked.

"Oh, my, no" said Mrs. Goose. "Just in the part that is over my bed."

"You could have moved your bed," said Mr. Goat.

"Why I did not even think of that," laughed Mrs. Goose. "I am silly."

When the roof was fixed, Mr. Goat gave Mrs. Goose the bill for his work.

"The next time you talk so much you will pay for that, too," he laughed.

Hetty's Singing

Hetty Hen lived on Wheat Farm.
All her neighbors and friends loved
her. She was so kind and good.

That is why Hetty was asked
to every party at the farm.

There was only one thing that the other
animals did not like about Hetty.

That was the way she sang. And
Hetty wanted to sing at every party.

Hetty thought that her singing
was very beautiful. "Ca-ku-ku-caw,
ca-ku-ku-caw!" she would sing,
just as loud as she could.

Hetty's neighbors and friends did not want to hurt her feelings. So they did not say anything to her about her singing.

But when she sang, it was so bad and so loud, her friends wanted to run away.

"She sings just like a crow," said Peter Pig. "And everyone knows that crows cannot sing."

One day, the animals on Wheat Farm heard that the king was coming to see them.

"That will be a big day for all of us," said Mrs. Duck. "But what will we do about Hetty? She will want to sing for the king."

"Maybe Hetty will get a cold before the king comes," said Peter Pig.

"Has Hetty ever heard herself sing?" asked Grandfather Goat.

"If she did, she would never sing again," said Gabriel Goose.

"Then I know how to stop her," said Grandfather Goat.

Grandfather Goat was very busy for the rest of that day.

He went to a store to get something. He came out with a big box and walked up the street.

Then he went to a card party. Hetty and some of her friends were there. And just as he thought, Hetty was singing as loud as she could.

That evening, all the animals on the farm met at Grandfather Goat's house. Hetty Hen was there, too.

"I have a big surprise for everyone," Grandfather Goat said. He showed them the big box.

Hetty looked very happy. She liked surprises.

Grandfather Goat reached into the box. He turned something on.

"Ca-ku-ku-caw, ca-ku-ku-caw," said the big box just as loud as it could.

"What is that? What is that?" asked Hetty as she put her wings over her ears.

"I thought that it would please you, Hetty," said Grandfather Goat. "That is your singing. You sang like this at the card party today."

"Well, turn it off," said Hetty. "I've never heard anything like it."

Hetty had been taught something. And after that day, she never sang again.

The king came to Wheat Farm. The band played for him.

Hetty made some beautiful cakes. They were so good! The king asked Hetty to make some for all of his friends.

How happy that made Hetty Hen!

Little Half Chick

Mother Hen looked at her family of five little chicks.

They were all good and beautiful. All but one. He was a bad little chick. He never liked to obey.

When Mother Hen called her chicks, this bad little chick looked around and then ran away.

He took food from the other chicks. He played when he should have been sleeping.

No one could do anything with him.

One day Mother Hen had a surprise. She found out that the bad little chick was only a half chick.

He had only one leg and one wing. He had only half a tail.

After breakfast one morning, Little Half Chick said to his mother, "Good-by. I am going to see the king."

Mother Hen looked sad. "Oh, my," she said. "What will happen to you out in the big world? You cannot even do as you are told here at home. You had better not go, Little Half Chick."

But Little Half Chick just shook his little half tail, and off he went.

On the way, Little Half Chick met
a little brook. There were many weeds
in it. And the water in the brook
could not run.

"Oh, please help me, Little Half
Chick," cried the brook. "Take these
weeds away so I can run."

Little Half Chick did not even stop.
He ran on and said, "I have no time
to take weeds away. I am off to see
the king today."

And he shook his little half tail
and went on his way.

Next Half Chick came to a fire that could not burn.

"Please put something on me to make me burn," the fire called out.

"I have no time to help you," said Half Chick. "I must be on my way. I am off to see the king today."

Again he shook his little half tail and went off on his one little leg.

Next Half Chick heard the wind crying.

"Please help me out of these trees," cried the wind.

But Half Chick said the same thing again. "I must be on my way. I am going to see the king today."

And he shook his little half tail and went on his way.

At last, Half Chick came
to the king's house.

The cook saw Half Chick and said,
"Oh, you are just what I want
for the king's dinner today."

The cook put Little Half Chick
into a big pot of water.

Half Chick jumped all around
in the pot. He cried, "Oh, water, please
do not burn me."

But the water said, "I wanted you
to take the weeds out of the brook,
so I could run. You would not help me.
Now I will punish you."

Half Chick asked the fire to help him.
"Please, fire, do not burn me," he cried
over and over again.

But the fire said, "I wanted you to help
me burn. But you did not have any time.
Now I will punish you."

And the fire jumped up around
the big black pot.

When the cook took the top off the pot,
the wind began to blow.

So Little Half Chick asked the wind
to help him. He cried, "Please, wind,
help me out of this pot. Please blow
me away."

"Oh, no, Little Chick," the wind said. "I wanted help, and you ran away."

The cook was just about to put the top back on the pot when the wind blew again.

This time he blew Little Half Chick right out of the pot and out of the house. He blew him to the top of a roof.

"There, now," said the wind to Half Chick. "That is the only place for a silly little chick like you."

Today Little Half Chick is up there, with his one leg and one wing. He can never again do as he pleases.

Can't you see him turn and turn as the wind blows?

Bobby Squirrel's Funny Tail

Bobby Squirrel sat up in a big tree.
There was not a thing in the world
that Bobby wanted to do.

He was too tired to move. He had been
busy looking for nuts all morning.

Blue Jay looked at the squirrel and saw
something funny. Then he sang,

"Bobby's tail is turning green.
It's the funniest tail I've ever seen!"

"Stop that and go away,"
Bobby Squirrel called to Blue Jay.
"My tail is all right."

"That is what you think," laughed Blue Jay. Then he began to sing again,

"Bobby's tail is turning green.

It's the funniest tail I've ever seen."

"Stop talking about my tail," said Bobby.

But Blue Jay went right on singing. He sang the same thing, over and over again.

Blue Jay turned the other way. At once Bobby looked back at his tail.

"Why, it is green," he said. "My beautiful tail is turning green."

Bobby began to feel very, very sad about his pretty tail.

Bobby ran over to see Mrs. Hen.

"Look, Mrs. Hen! My tail is turning green," he cried.

"Good heavens!" said Mrs. Hen. "Why do you frighten people like that?"

"But just look at my tail," said Bobby. "You would frighten people, too, if you had a green tail."

Now all this time Blue Jay sat up in the tree singing,

"Bobby's tail is turning green.

It's the funniest tail I've ever seen."

Mrs. Hen looked at Bobby's tail. "It does not look so funny," she said. "The green gives your tail a new look."

"But I don't want a new look," the squirrel said.

Then he thought maybe his legs would turn green. Maybe he would turn green all over!

Bobby Squirrel went in a hurry to tell Peter Rabbit about his tail.

"What have you been eating?" asked Peter Rabbit.

"Nuts! Only nuts!" said Bobby.

"They must be turning your tail green. Maybe you should stop eating nuts," said Peter Rabbit.

That made Bobby very sad. He liked nuts more than anything in the world. So Bobby went to see Mr. King.

Mr. King worked in a place where
they fixed cars. He always had nuts
for Bobby. So Bobby liked him.

Mr. King saw Bobby's tail and said,
"Where have you been, Bobby? You have
green paint all over your tail."

Then Mr. King put something
on Bobby's tail, and the green paint came
right off.

Bobby was happy again. He could eat
nuts and he could have a pretty tail, too.

He ran back to the tree near the brook
to find Blue Jay.

But Blue Jay was too tired to talk
any more. He only said, "Good, good!"

Farm Neighbors

A Surprise for Joan and Mark

Joan and Mark went to stay with their aunt and uncle who lived on a farm.

They had been there three days. One morning, Mark said, "Aunt Mary, Joan and I must go home tomorrow."

Aunt Mary looked surprised.

"But you just came the other day," she said. "Why must you go back home tomorrow? Are you homesick? Do you miss your friends in the city?"

"We like it here on the farm,"
said Mark. "We would like to stay here
all the time, but Joan and I must
go to Mass on Sunday. So we had better
go home tomorrow."

Aunt Mary laughed. "Uncle Tom and
I go to Mass on Sunday," she told Mark.

"Where do you go?" Mark asked.
"There is no church out here."

"Yes, there is. We have a pretty
little church," said Aunt Mary. "And
it is not very far from here.

"We will take you and Joan to Mass
with us on Sunday."

Sunday morning came, and it was time
to go to church. Uncle Tom told
Joan and Mark to go out and pick
some flowers from the garden.

After the children had picked
the flowers, they got into the car
to ride to church. They did not go far
before Uncle Tom stopped the car.

"Well, here is our little church,"
said Aunt Mary.

"My, what a small church!" said Mark.

"Not many people live out this way,"
Uncle Tom told the children. "So we
do not need a big church to have
Our Lord in the Mass."

When the children walked
into the church, they saw the altar.
Everything looked so small.

Aunt Mary put the flowers on the altar.

Soon after that, the Mass began.

Joan and Mark were surprised again.
The Mass was just the same as in their
church in the city.

On the way home, Uncle Tom said,
"Our Lord comes on the altar in every
Mass. He does not care if the church
is big or small. He cares only about us.
He loves to be with us."

The Tooseys on the Farm

It was raining. So all the little Tooseys had to play in the house.

They were all running after their dog named Star. And Star was running after a kitten.

Bow-wow! Bow-wow!

Bang! Bang! Down went a chair.

Clang! Clang! Down went some dishes.

"Look, Mother," cried Timmy as loud as he could. "See what Star did!"

"Oh, this house is too small for all of us," Mother Toosey said.

"I think we shall move. I will find a house on the farm. Then you can run around without running into someone."

After two weeks, all the little Tooseys were running in and out of a big yellow farm house.

Then they ran around all their land to look at the rest of the farm.

"Mother, Mother, look here," called Peter. "We have a big barn that is painted red. There is not a thing in it."

"There is a green hen house too," said Ted. "We need some hens to put in it."

"We need a goat, too," said Ann. "We can't live on a farm without a goat."

"Maybe Daddy will get us a cow, some hens, and a goat," said Mother . "Let's write him a letter. He will be coming home from the city next Sunday."

"Who will write the letter?" asked Timmy.

"I am too busy," said Mother.

"I don't know how to write very well," said Ann.

"And I don't write very well at all," said Bobby.

"And we are too little to write," said all the other little Tooseys.

The next day, Ted began to write the letter. This is what he said:

Dear Daddy,

We have a big red cow that needs a barn in it. We have a green hen house that needs a long tail so it can moo. We need a quack that can goat.

Mother began to read the letter.

"Oh, dear," she laughed. "You have mixed everything up. Daddy will not know what we are talking about."

So Ted began the letter again. As Ted began to write, all the other Tooseys told him what to say.

This is what the next letter said:

Dear Daddy,

Please bring us a green cow that gives white milk. Please bring us some hens with long red tails, and a little goat that can cock-a-doodle like a quack.

Mother began to read the letter.

"This is a little better than the other one," she said. "It is not too mixed up. Maybe Daddy will know what we want."

"Why don't we make pictures of the things we want?" asked Timmy. "Then Daddy can see from the pictures what we are trying to tell him."

So Timmy made a picture of a cow,
a picture of a goat, and a picture
of three hens.

Daddy Toosey must have looked
at the pictures. He did not get things
mixed up.

He came home in a big truck. And he
had everything the family had asked for.
There was a cow for the barn
that was painted red, three hens for the
green hen house, and a little goat.

Who Took the Pumpkins?

Grandmother Gold lived all by herself on a little farm.

One day, she thought she would make a pie. "Now, let's see. What kind shall it be?" she asked herself.

"Oh, I know," she said. "It will be a pumpkin pie."

So Grandmother went to the garden to get a pumpkin.

"This is funny," she thought. "Just last week, there were many pumpkins here! Now there is not one. Someone took them. That is what happened."

Grandmother became sad and walked to the house.

On the way, she met the mailman who had a letter for her.

"Have you been weeding your garden?" the mailman asked.

"No, I went to the garden to get a pumpkin," Grandmother told him. "But someone came into my garden and took every last one of them!"

The mailman laughed and said, "I shall never forget the time you lost your light bill. You said that I did not bring it. But you found it that same day in your apron pocket."

"Well, I will not find the pumpkins in my apron pocket," Grandmother said.

She began to think about another kind of pie. Just then, Mr. Fox came to fix the barn door.

Grandmother told him all about the pumpkins. She told him what she had told the mailman. She said that someone took them.

"I saw someone in your garden the other day," said Mr. Fox. "But don't forget the time you were mixed up. You thought you had lost your glasses and you had them on!"

"That was very funny," laughed Grandmother. "I never shall forget that day. Everything was mixed up."

Grandmother sat down in her chair. Ting-a-ling went the telephone. It was Mrs. Star, one of the neighbors.

"Do you have three or four eggs for me?" she asked. "I need them to make some cookies. I shall pay you back just as soon as I get some more."

"Why, yes," said Grandmother. "You can have as many eggs as you want."

Then Grandmother Gold thought of something.

"Mrs. Star!" she said. "Did I ask you for three or four eggs the other day?"

"Yes, you did," said Mrs. Star. "You said that you had so many pumpkins you did not know what to do with them."

"That is it," said Grandmother.

"You wanted to make them into pies
for Saint Ann's Children's Home," said
Mrs. Star. "So you asked me for eggs."

"That's right," said Grandmother.
"That is where all my pumpkins went.
I used them for pumpkin pies. Oh, dear!
I did forget that I used them."

So Grandmother did not make
a pumpkin pie. She made an apple pie.
And all the time she laughed and
laughed about the mix up.

Uncle Tom's Surprise

Kathy liked to stay on the farm.
She always had fun there.

So one day, Kathy's daddy took her
to the farm. Aunt Mary met her
at the door.

"Hello, I am so happy to be here,"
said Kathy when the door opened. "What
is new? Does Uncle Tom have
any new baby animals?"

"Yes, there are some new baby chicks and four baby pigs," said Aunt Mary. "Uncle Tom has something which he likes very much. He made it himself. He will want to show it to you."

"Where is Uncle Tom?" asked Kathy.

"He must be in the barn," said Aunt Mary. "Run down there and you will find him."

"That is what I shall do," said Kathy. And off she ran to find Uncle Tom.

"Hello, Uncle Tom," cried Kathy when she got to the barn.

"I've been waiting for you," said Uncle Tom. "Would you like to name our new baby calf?"

"A baby calf!" cried Kathy.

"Aunt Mary did not tell me about that. She said there were some new baby chicks and pigs."

"Well, the calf just came today," said Uncle Tom. "Come and see it."

Then Uncle Tom took Kathy to another part of the barn.

"What a black calf! She is blacker than any calf I've ever seen," said Kathy. "Let's name her Blacker."

"That is a funny name," laughed Uncle Tom. "Blacker she shall be."

Then Kathy thought about what her aunt had told her. "Aunt Mary said that you had a big surprise to show me. It is something you made and like very much," she said.

Uncle Tom smiled. "Oh, yes, that is right," he said. "Come and see what I have made. It is a talking well."

"Oh, Uncle Tom," laughed Kathy. "A well can't talk."

"This one can," said Uncle Tom.

Uncle Tom and Kathy walked
down the hill. Soon they came
to the new well. There was a little roof
over it.

Kathy looked down into the well.

"Say something to the well," said
Uncle Tom.

Kathy said, "Good morning!"

Up from the well came the same words
she used, "Good morning!"

"Why, the well does talk," cried
the little girl.

"That's right," said Uncle Tom.

"The well talks back to you. It says
the same words you say."

"This is fun," said Kathy. "I want to try it again."

"Good-by, we are going now," she called into the well.

"Good-by, we are going now," the well called back.

Then Uncle Tom told Kathy something. He told her why her own words came back from the well.

Do you know why?

The Cows' Shawl

Betty had never seen a real cow or a real calf. She had never seen a real pig or a real goat.

Betty lived in the city. So the only farm animals she had ever seen were in picture books.

One day, Betty's father took her to see some friends who lived on a farm.

Mr. Bangs, the farmer, took Betty around to see the animals.

"Do cows wear shawls?" Betty asked.

Mr. Bangs looked at her. "Why, no!" he said. "Why do you ask that?"

"I heard Mrs. Bangs talking to Bob," Betty said. "She said if he wanted to milk the cows, he had better get their shawl."

The farmer laughed. "Bob is a new man. He is working for us," he said. "He is milking the cows now. Let's go to the barn and see what is going on."

"Yes, let's!" said Betty. "The only cows I ever saw were in picture books. But not one was wearing a shawl."

Farmer Bangs laughed again. "You
will not see any cows wearing shawls
around here," he said.

By that time, they had reached
the barn. When they went in, Betty was
too surprised to say another word. She
just laughed and laughed and laughed.

There was Bob, milking a cow. The
cow was not wearing a shawl, but Bob
was. And just think of it! The shawl
was red and green!

"How funny!" laughed Betty. "Why
is Bob wearing that silly looking shawl?"

"An old woman used to own these two cows," said Farmer Bangs. "She always had on a shawl like that when she milked them.

"When the cows came here, they would not give any milk. They missed the old woman's shawl. We had to get one just like it and use it.

"So we call it the cows' shawl," said Mr. Bangs. "Anyone who milks these two cows must wear the shawl."

Betty laughed again. "That is one of the funniest things I have ever seen," she said. "Not even my picture books have anything so funny in them."

Jean and the Bookmobile

Jean Long was up with the birds. She put on a clean dress. Her mother fixed her hair. She said her morning prayers and went down to breakfast.

Jean was going to Saint Ann's School with Mary Ann who lived on the next farm.

The bookmobile was coming to school today. Mary Ann told Jean all about it.

"The bookmobile is a library. It is taken from one school to another in a big truck," said Mary Ann. "It is a good thing for people who live on farms. Sometimes they live far from a library."

Jean's grandmother thought
the bookmobile was the best thing she
had ever heard about.

And Jean's mother said, "I wish
the bookmobile would have books
for mothers and fathers."

Jean was happy. Now she could get
a book of her own. She wanted one
with many pictures in it.

When Mary Ann and Jean got to
school, the bookmobile was there.

All the children were looking
for the books they wanted to read.

No one saw Jean walk around
to the back door of the truck.

There she found a big animal book.
In it were pictures of cows, horses,
goats, pigs, and even elephants.

Jean looked at every picture. Then
she became tired and went to sleep.

Soon it was time for the bookmobile
to move on to the next school.

When they got there, Miss Cook
opened the doors of the bookmobile.
She went in to get some books to show
the children.

What a surprise she had!

There was Jean sleeping. She had a big animal book in her hands.

"Oh, dear!" cried Miss Cook. "Where did you come from?"

"I do not know which picture book I want," said Jean. "Maybe I would like the one about boats and jet planes."

"You are far from home," Miss Cook told the little girl. "I will hurry up with these children. Then I will take you back to Saint Ann's School."

Jean thought it was fun to ride in a bookmobile.

"You like books, don't you, Jean?" Miss Cook asked.

"Yes, I do," said Jean. "My mother and grandmother like them, too. They would like to have some books. They wish that the bookmobile would have books for mothers and fathers to read."

"They do?" said Miss Cook. "Maybe we can bring some books for them the next time we come."

When the bookmobile got back to Saint Ann's School, Mary Ann was waiting for Jean.

"Hop in," Miss Cook told Mary Ann. "I will take you and Jean home."

When they reached Jean's home, Miss Cook talked to Mother and Grandmother.

"I stopped to ask if you would like to have the bookmobile bring books for you, too," Miss Cook said.

"We would be so happy if it could," said Mother.

"It will," said Miss Cook. "Come over to Saint Ann's School with Mary Ann and Jean next week. I will have good books for all of you. Tell the neighbors to come, too."

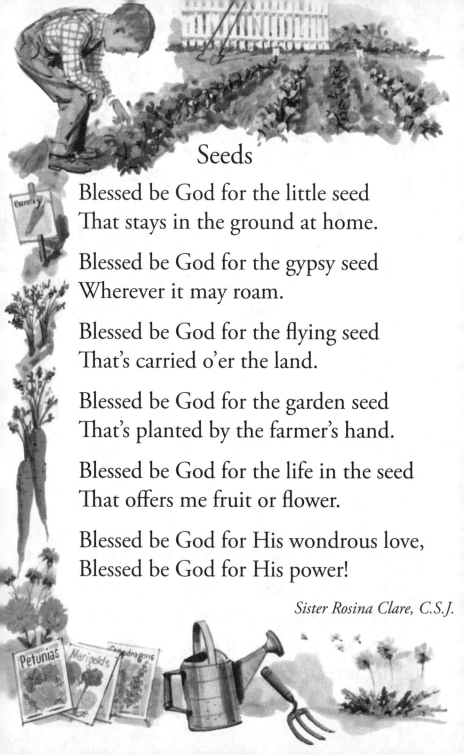

Seeds

Blessed be God for the little seed
That stays in the ground at home.

Blessed be God for the gypsy seed
Wherever it may roam.

Blessed be God for the flying seed
That's carried o'er the land.

Blessed be God for the garden seed
That's planted by the farmer's hand.

Blessed be God for the life in the seed
That offers me fruit or flower.

Blessed be God for His wondrous love,
Blessed be God for His power!

Sister Rosina Clare, C.S.J.

Stories We All Like

The Little Fir Tree

Why the Little Tree Was Sad

There was once a little fir tree that lived in the big woods with many other trees. This little tree was very sad.

Some of the big trees looked down on the little tree and made fun of him.

"Oh, just see how big and beautiful we are," they would say. "We can do all kinds of things you can't do.

"The birds make their nests in us.
They never come near you."

This made the little fir tree very sad.

"I wish I could be big and beautiful,"
thought the little tree. "I wish that
I could be as happy as the other trees.
Why must I be so sad?"

It began to grow dark in the woods.
All the trees went to sleep. All but
the little tree.

Then something happened.

The woods became as light as day.

The little fir tree looked around,
and there he saw a beautiful fairy.

The other trees were all sleeping.
Not one of them saw the fairy.

The little tree did not want the fairy
to see him because he was not pretty.

"I will not move," he said to himself. "The fairy will think that I am sleeping, too."

The beautiful fairy came right up to the little tree and smiled.

"Hello, my little friend," she said. "Why are you so sad? Tell me what I can do to make you happy. I will give you anything you wish for."

How surprised and happy the little tree was when he heard that!

He looked at the kind fairy and said, "I wish that I were big and beautiful like the other trees in the woods.

"I do not want to be a fir tree. I want to be some other kind of tree. I want all the other trees to look at me and like me."

The kind fairy looked sad when the little tree said this.

"Oh, little tree," she said. "I cannot make you into another kind of tree.

"God made you a fir tree. That is what He wants you to be."

"You told me to make a wish. Why can't I have what I want?" asked Little Fir Tree.

The little tree began to cry. "Oh, if only someone would cut me down and take me out of the woods," he said. "Maybe I would be happy then."

The fairy saw how sad the little tree was, and she said, "I have come here to make you happy. You want to be beautiful so that others will look at you. You will never be happy that way.

"God made you to be a good little fir tree. You can only be happy that way.

"Be kind to others. Let the birds make their nests in you.

"Let little children sing and play around you.

"Always be a good little fir tree because that is what God made you.

"Someday, God will give you something great to do."

Then the beautiful fairy went away.

How the Little Fir Tree Became Great

The days and nights came and went.
The little fir tree did not forget
what the fairy had told him.

Many of the big trees in the woods
had been cut down and taken away.

The little fir tree tried to be good.
He tried to do all that the fairy
had said.

The birds made their nests in him.

Little children laughed and played
around the little tree.

All day long, he heard the birds sing
and the children laugh.

Sometimes a tired man sat down
near the tree to rest.

Little Fir Tree began to feel happy.

Day after day, he thought about
the great thing God would give him to do.

Then one day he saw a man and
some children coming into the woods.

"We know which tree we want, Daddy,"
the children said to their father.

"This fir tree is the best tree
in the woods."

"It is very beautiful," said
the father. "Let's cut it down and take
it home."

That evening Little Fir Tree
was put into a big room. There was
a gold star at its very top.

Many little children looked at it.

Little Fir Tree heard the children
as they sang.

The little tree was once so sad,
but now he was very, very happy.

God had given the little fir tree
something great to do.

That was to make others happy
on the birthday of Our Lord.

The Soldier Saint

Martin is now a great saint in heaven.
But a long time ago, he once lived
in this world just as we do.

Martin was a very kind man. He loved
the poor. He gave them everything
he could.

If he had good food, he gave
that away. If he had money, he gave
it away. Sometimes, he even gave away
his best clothes.

His friends knew that Martin was
very kind to the poor. Some of them
did not like this very much.

One day long ago, his soldiers gave
Saint Martin a beautiful red cloak.

"If you love us, you will always
keep this cloak," they told him.

Martin laughed and thanked
his friends for the cloak.

"I will keep it just as long as I can,"
he said.

The soldiers said, "Well, we shall wait
and see how long that is."

For many weeks, Martin wore
the new cloak. He liked it very much.

One cold night, Martin rode home
on his white horse. He was very
cold and tired.

"How good this warm cloak feels
on a night like this," Martin thought,
as the cold wind blew around him.

When Martin came near his home,
the horse began to go very, very fast.
Then all at once the horse stopped.

Martin did not know what had
happened. He looked around. Then,
in the dark, he saw a poor man.

The man had no cloak. His clothes were old, and he shook with the cold.

"I have told my soldiers that I would keep this warm cloak," Martin said to himself. "But that poor man is cold and his clothes are so old. I must think of some way to help him."

Martin thought and prayed.

"Oh, I know what I can do," he said. "I will cut my cloak in half. Part of it will keep the poor man warm. And I will have the other half to show my men."

So Martin cut the cloak in two. He put half of it around the poor man.

Then he got back on his horse
and rode off.

When Saint Martin got home, one
of the soldiers said, "Martin, look
at your cloak. Someone has cut it."

"Yes," said Martin. "I cut it."

"Did you give away part of your cloak?"
one man asked.

"Yes, I did," said Saint Martin.
"It is keeping someone warm
on this cold night."

Then he said good night to his men.

That night, as Martin was sleeping,
the poor man he had helped came
to his bed.

He did not look like a poor man now.
He was Jesus, the Son of God.

Our Lord looked at Martin and said,
"I am the poor Man you helped this night.
Your cloak is keeping Me warm.

What you do to others, Martin, you do
to Me."

The Story of Saint Bernadette

The Beautiful Lady

Bernadette was a girl who lived long ago. Like Martin, she is now a saint in heaven.

Bernadette's family was very poor. They did not even have a house of their own to live in.

Many times there was little food for the children to eat. Their clothes were poor and patched.

One day, Bernadette's mother said, "We need some more wood for the fire. Will you go and get some, Bernadette? Take Marie with you."

So Bernadette and her sister Marie started out to find some wood.

On the way, they met one of the neighbor children.

"I will go with you," she said. "If three of us work, it will not take so long."

In the woods, the children came to a brook. Marie and her friend took off their shoes and walked in the water.

Bernadette took off one shoe. Then she started to take off the other shoe. Just then the wind began to blow.

"That is funny," she thought. "There was no wind before."

The girl looked all around. It did not look like rain. Not a tree moved.

Then the wind blew again. It seemed to come from a place where there were many big rocks.

Bernadette looked at the rocks. Then she saw something which she had never seen before.

There, on a big rock, was a beautiful Lady in white. Bernadette had never seen anyone so beautiful.

She became frightened.

"Who is that beautiful Lady?" she asked herself. "How did she get here?"

Then the beautiful Lady began to pray the Rosary.

Bernadette took her own rosary from her apron pocket. She prayed the Rosary with the beautiful Lady.

After that, the beautiful Lady called
Bernadette to come nearer. But the girl
was too frightened to move.

She looked at the ground. When
she looked up again, the beautiful Lady
was not there.

On the way home, Bernadette asked
Marie and her friend if they had seen
the Lady.

But they had not seen her. They each
laughed at Bernadette and said she
was silly.

Bernadette could not forget what she
had seen. She knew now that the Lady
in white was Mary, the Mother of God.

What Our Lady Wanted

Bernadette thought about the
Lady the first thing in the morning. She
thought of her the last thing at night.
Again and again, she prayed the Rosary.

Each day she went back to the place
near the rocks where she had seen Mary.
Sometimes many other people went
with her just to see what would happen.

No one but Bernadette saw
the Mother of God. No one but Bernadette
heard what Mary said.

One morning, Bernadette was at the
place near the rocks. She took out
her rosary and prayed.

All at once, she saw dear Mother Mary.

This time, Mary told the girl to make
a hole in the ground with her hands.

Bernadette did as she was told.
At once, the water began to come out
of the little hole.

Then Mary told Bernadette to tell
the priest and the people what
had happened.

"Tell them that I want a church
in this place," she said.

The people laughed at Bernadette.
Many of them said that she had not
heard anything. They said she only
thought she had.

At last the priest did what Bernadette
wanted.

That was long ago.

Today there is a beautiful big church where Bernadette once saw the Mother of God.

The water that comes out of the ground near the rocks has made many sick people well again.

Bernadette is a saint in heaven. Now she can see Jesus and His Mother each day for ever and ever.

Saint Francis and the Birds

There once lived a very good man named Francis. He is now a saint in heaven.

Saint Francis lived in this world, long ago. He loved God very, very much. He showed this love by being kind to others.

He was kind to the birds, the animals, and the flowers. He was kind to everything that God made.

Saint Francis sometimes called them his little brothers and sisters.

One day, Saint Francis was walking near the woods. He heard the cry of a bird.

"That bird must be hurt," he thought.

So the saint went to see what had happened to one of his brothers.

When he reached the brook, the saint found a little brown bird on the ground. The bird's wing seemed to be hurt. She did not fly away.

The saint picked up the bird. As he did so, a small boy came running out of the woods.

The boy seemed to have something in his cap. He did not want anyone to see what it was.

"Good morning, little brother," said Saint Francis to the boy. "What do you have in your cap?"

The boy did not say anything. He would not let the saint see what he had.

Then Saint Francis showed him the bird in his hand.

"This bird seems to be hurt," he said. "But she is not hurt. She is frightened. Something must have happened to one of her baby birds."

The little boy would not look
at the good saint. He looked down
at the ground. He did not say one word.

"Sometimes a mother bird does things
just to make people forget about her
little ones," said Saint Francis.
"In that way, she saves them from
being hurt."

Just then the little boy's cap moved.
And Saint Francis saw a poor little
baby bird. The bird tried to get out.

"Oh, little brother!" said Saint Francis
to the boy. "You have taken that
baby bird from its nest. What are you
going to do with it?"

"I want to take it home with me," said
the little boy. "My father will make
a house for it to live in. I will take care
of it. I will let it sing for me. Maybe
some day the little bird will love me."

"But the mother bird loves her little one," the saint said. "See how she is trying to get it back to her.

"God did not make these birds to live in a house. He made them to live out here in the woods."

The boy looked sad. "But I love this little bird," he said.

"If you love it, you will let it go to its mother," Saint Francis told him.

So the boy opened his cap. Away flew the little bird. Then the saint opened his hands. Away flew the mother bird.

Soon the two birds came back.
They wanted to fly near Saint Francis.
Each of them seemed to thank the
good saint for what he did for them.

Before Saint Francis said good-by
to the little boy, he told him something.

"That baby bird will come back to you,
little brother," he said.

And every morning after that, the
little bird came to sing to the little boy.

The Birds

When Jesus Christ was four years old,
The angels brought Him toys of gold,
Which no man had ever bought or sold.

And yet with these He would not play,
He made Himself small fowl of clay,
And blessed them till they flew away.

Jesus Christ, Thou Child so wise,
Bless mine hands and fill my eyes,
And bring my soul to paradise.

Hilaire Belloc

245

Who Is My Neighbor?

One day Our Lord taught the people how to love God. He told them how to be kind to their neighbors, too.

A man who heard Jesus asked, "But who is my neighbor?"

Then Jesus told this story.

There was once a good man who started out on a long trip to another city.

As he walked down the road, he met some robbers. They hurt him. Then they took all his money and ran away

The poor hurt man stayed near
the side of the road. He could not move.

After a long time, he heard someone
coming down the road. "Now I will get
some help," the poor man thought to himself.

He called out as loud as he could.

The stranger who was coming down
the road was not a kind man. He did
not like other people. He thought only
of himself.

The stranger stopped when he heard
the cry. He looked down and saw
that the hurt man could not move.

But the stranger did not feel sad when he saw the poor man. He just looked at him and went on his way.

The poor man was very sad. He was frightened too. Would he have to stay there all night by himself?

After a time, he again heard someone coming down the road.

"I know that I shall get some help now," he thought to himself.

"Please help me," he cried out.

The stranger heard the cry, but he would not even go near the hurt man. He only looked at him and walked away.

It began to grow dark. The poor man became more and more frightened. He knew that no one would walk on this road after dark.

Then he again heard something, but it did not seem to be a man.

"That seems to be a mule,"
the hurt man thought. "Someone
must be coming by on a mule. Maybe
thc rider will help me."

He called for help.

The mule seemed to be coming nearer
and nearer. Then all at once, it stopped.

The hurt man looked up and saw
a man from another land.

"This man will never help me," he
thought to himself. "He is from another
land. His people and my people do not
even like each other."

When the stranger saw that the poor
man was hurt, he jumped off his mule.

He tried to help the poor man get up
from the ground.

"I cannot walk," the hurt man told
the stranger. "Thank you for trying
to help me. You must go on your way
before it gets too dark."

"I shall never go on without you,"
said the stranger.

Then he picked up the hurt man
and put him on the mule's back.

"We will go to the next city," he said.

In the city, the stranger found a place where people could stay over night. He gave the owner some money.

"Keep this poor hurt man and take care of him," he said. "When he is better, he can go on his way again."

Then the stranger said good-by to the hurt man and went on to his own land.

After Jesus had told this story, He looked at the man who had asked, "Who is my neighbor?"

"Which of the three men in the story was a real neighbor to the hurt man?" Jesus asked.

"The one who helped him and was kind to him," said the man.

Our Lord then said, "Go now and do the same to your neighbor."

Christ Our King.

The Christ-Child stood at Mary's knee,
His hair was like a crown,
    And all the flowers looked up at Him,
And all the stars looked down.

G. K. Chesterton

To the Teacher

These Are Our Neighbors, Revised Edition, is the Initial Second Reader, of the FAITH AND FREEDOM Basic Readers. It is adapted to meet the needs and abilities of children in the first half of the second grade.

This reader introduces 227 new words, 171 of which (starred in the list below) can be recognized independently through application of the various word-recognition techniques devel-oped in the teaching manuals of the preceding books of the series and reviewed in the manual accompanying this second reader. The 324 words taught in the first-grade level of the series are repeated and maintained in this book.

Training in the virtues of Christian social living is given through interesting story material centering around the young child's experiences in the home, the neighborhood, the parish school and church, and the wider community. The ideal of obedience, as exemplified in the lives of Christ, the Blessed Virgin, and Saint Joseph, is applied to the child's private as well as to his social life. Acceptance of the Divine Will as the source of all authority, filial devotion to parents, due respect for authority in the community, regard for the rights of others, and a realization of the spiritual values of life are stressed throughout the book.

WORD LIST

UNIT I

7. together

8. Mark
   Joan*
9. shoe
10. Kevin*
    Kathy
11. Denis*
12. small*

-----

13. twins*
14. game*
15. parade
16. . . .
17. cracker*
18. . . .
19. band*

-----

20. started

21. light*
22. stopped*
    policeman
23. can't*
    obey

-----

24. *(Poem)*

-----

25. beautiful
26. heaven
    happened*
27. let*
    bad*
28. . . .
29. . . .

-----

30. *(Poem)*

-----

31. ever*
    seen*

32. wash
33. very
    tried*
35. . . .
36. . . .

-----

37. wait*
    trip*
38. week*
39. long*
40. save*
    shall*
41. talked*
    Lake*
42. . . .

-----

43. merry-go-
    round*
    horse*
44. elephants*
    tickets*

45. around
46. jet*
    planes*
47. . . .
48. . . .

-----

49. move
50. way*
51. part*
52. any*
53. . . .

-----

54. . . .

UNIT II

55. neighbors

-----

56. *(Poem)*

254

57. Patches*
   their
58. always*
   over
59. first*
   three*
60. four*
   five*
61. fairy*
   last*
62. these*
   real*
----
63. please*
64. right*
   feel*
65. telephone
   hello*
66. pay*
   hurt*
67. say*
----
68 cards*
   mailbox*
69. never*
70. Miss*
   thought
71. found*
   only
72. Mr.*
   chair*
73. smiled*
   coming*
----
74. Robber*
Bob*
75. even
   near*
76. . . .
77. again
   been
78. . . .
----
79. Uncle
80. stories*
   leg*
81. better*
   think*

82. altar
83. . . .
84. . . .
----
85. wise*
   owl
86. flew*
   rain*
87. pick*
88. cried*
89. top*
   pie*
90. . . .

UNIT III

91. . . .
----
92. library
93. let's *
   knew
94. o'clock*
95. boats*
96. Brooks*
   herself*
97. himself*
   than*
----
98. once
99. dark*
100. king*
   land*
101. . . .
102. own
103. . . .
----
104. city
105. stars*
106. sky*
   black*
107. reach*
   dear*
108. door*
   opened*
----
109. taught
110. fixed*

hair*
111. painting*
112. Mass*
   Marie
113. Doctor*
114. clothes
   need*
----
115. glasses*
116. barn*
117. silly*
118. cat*
   coat*
119. clean*
----
120. (Poem)

UNIT IV

121..
----
122. garden*
123. beans*
   evening*
124. carrots
125. should*
126. prize*
   funniest*
127. pumpkins*
----
128. Hacker* busy
129. butter*
130..
131..
132..
133. ice cream*
   much*
----
134. soldier
   flags*
135..
136. don't
137. gold*
   pin*
138..
----

139. monkey
140 flying*
   waved*
141..
142.turned*
   does
143..
144.hand*
145..

146.Cook* hurry *
147..
148. side*
149. cold*
   punish*
150..
151..

152.(Poem)

UNIT V

153..

154.apron
   cap*
155..
156. wee*
157. wish*
158. wings*
----
159. sang*
160. pot* roof*
161. tomorrow
162..
163..
----
164. Hetty's*
   loud
165.Grand-
   father*
166..
167..
168. I've*
----
169. half
170. tail*

255

shook*	pictures	214. *(Poem)*	233. Rosary
171. weeds*	192. ...	----------------------	234. each*
burn*	----------------------	UNIT VII	235. ...
173. ...	193. ...	215. ...	236. ...
174. ...	194.became*	----------------------	237. ...
175. blew*	195. ...	216. fir*	238. ...
----------------------	196. ...	woods*	----------------------
176. Jay*	197. used*	217. ...	239. Francis
177. frighten*	----------------------	218. ...	brothers*
179. ...	198. ...	219. ...	240. ...
180. ...	199. which*	220.great	241. ...
----------------------	200. calf*	221. ...	242. ...
UNIT VI	201. ...	222. ...	243. ...
181..	202.words*	223. ...	244. ...
----------------------	203. ...	----------------------	----------------------
182. stay*	----------------------	224. Martin*	245. *(Poem)*
aunt	204.shawl	ago*	----------------------
183. Sunday*	wear	225. cloak*	246. road*
184. ...	205. ...	keep*	247. stranger
185. Lord*	206. ...	226. warm	248. ...
186. or*	207. ...	227. ...	249.mule*
----------------------	----------------------	228. ...	250. ...
187. Tooseys	208. bookmo-	229. ...	251. ...
running*	bile	----------------------	252. ...
188. ...	209. ...	230. Berna-	----------------------
189. write	210. ...	dette	253. *(Poem)*
letter*	211. ...	Lady*	
190. mixed*	212. ...	231. ...	
191. bring*	213. ...	232. seemed*	
	----------------------	rocks*	

ACKNOWLEDGMENTS (continued)

Acknowledgment is also made to *Child Life* magazine for "The Dog's Dark Days," from "The Hound that Had a Headache," by Bess B. Green, copyright 1951, and "Garden Surprises," from "The Man Who Mixed the Seeds," by Rebecca K. Sprinkle, copyright 1952; Child Train-ing Association, publishers of *Children's Activities,* for "Traffic Light," by Nona Keen Duffy, copyright 1952, and "At the Barber's Shop," by Bette Killion, copyright 1953; F. A. Owen Publishing Company for "My Literary Dog," by Elise de Saint Andre, copyright 1955 by F. A. Owen Publishing Company, and reprinted from *The Instructor by* permission; Publications for Catholic Youth for "Run-Away Tom-Tom," and for "Seeds," by Sister Rosina Clare, C.S.J., reprinted from *Mine Two* magazine; Jean Horton Berg for "Mary Ann Gets a Hair Cut," from "Jeanie's Haircut," *Child Life* magazine, copyright 1951; Mabel G. LaRue for an adaptation of "The Tooseys on the Farm," from "The Tooseys."

CDEFGHIJ 06987654

PRINTED IN THE UNITED STATES OF AMERICA